Pop Hits

Wise Publications
London/New York/Paris/Sydney/Copenhagen/Berlin/Madrid/Tokyo

Exclusive Distributors:
Music Sales Limited
8/9 Frith Street, London W1D 3JB, England.
Music Sales Pty Limited
120 Rothschild Avenue, Rosebery, NSW 2018, Australia.

Order No. AM972213
ISBN 0-7119-9115-4
This book © Copyright 2002 by Wise Publications

Compiled by Nick Crispin
Music arranged by Roger Day
Music processed by Enigma Music Production Services
Cover photograph (Will Young) courtesy of London Features International

Printed in the United Kingdom by
Printwise (Haverhill) Limted, Suffolk

Your Guarantee of Quality
As publishers, we strive to produce every book to the highest commercial standards.
The music has been freshly engraved and the book has been carefully designed to minimise
awkward page turns and to make playing from it a real pleasure.
Particular care has been given to specifying acid-free, neutral-sized paper made from pulps
which have not been elemental chlorine bleached. This pulp is from farmed sustainable forests
and was produced with special regard for the environment.
Throughout, the printing and binding have been planned to ensure a sturdy, attractive publication
which should give years of enjoyment.
If your copy fails to meet our high standards, please inform us and we will gladly replace it.

www.musicsales.com

Can't Get You Out Of My Head *Kylie Minogue* 4

Caught In The Middle *A1* 8

Emotion *Destiny's Child* 28

Evergreen *Will Young* 12

Hero *Enrique Iglesias* 16

If You Come Back *Blue* 20

Somethin' Stupid *Robbie Williams / Nicole Kidman* 24

Unchained Melody *Gareth Gates* 33

What If *Kate Winslet* 36

World Of Our Own *Westlife* 44

You *S Club 7* 40

Can't Get You Out Of My Head

Words & Music by Cathy Dennis & Rob Davis

La la la la la la la la la la la la la la la la

la la la la la la la la la la la la la. I just

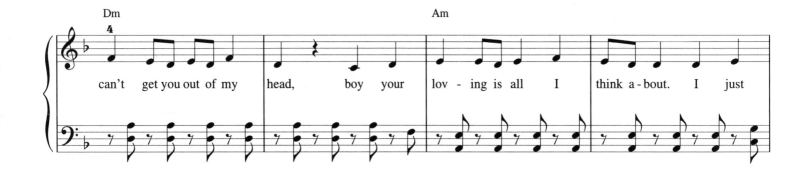

can't get you out of my head, boy your lov - ing is all I think a - bout. I just

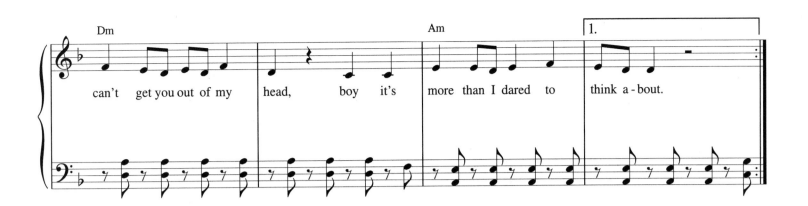

can't get you out of my head, boy it's more than I dared to think a-bout.

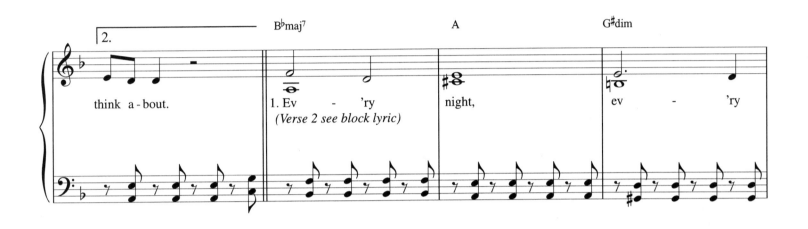

think a-bout. 1. Ev - 'ry night, ev - 'ry

(Verse 2 see block lyric)

day___ just to___ be there in___ your arms._____ Won't you___

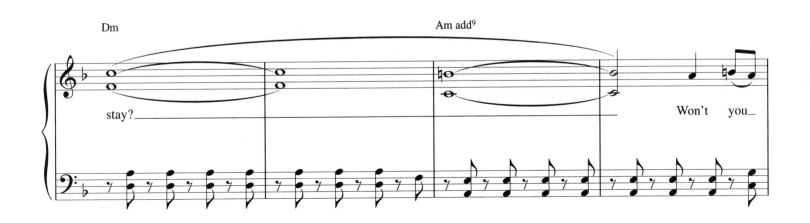

stay?_____ Won't you___

5

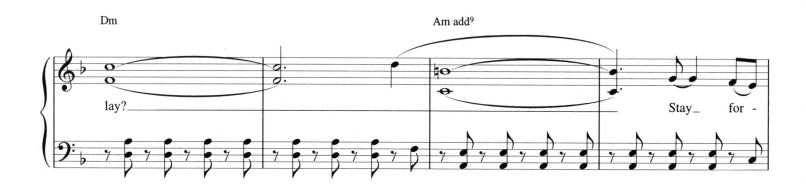

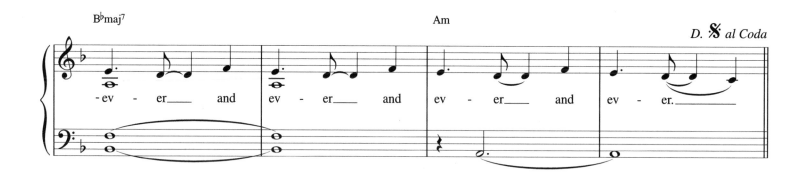

CODA

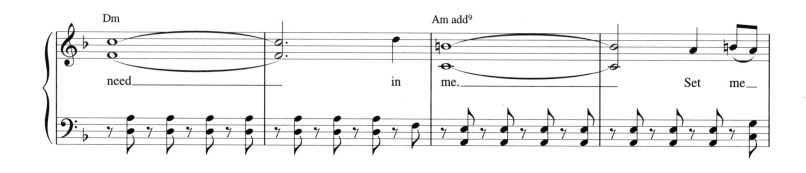

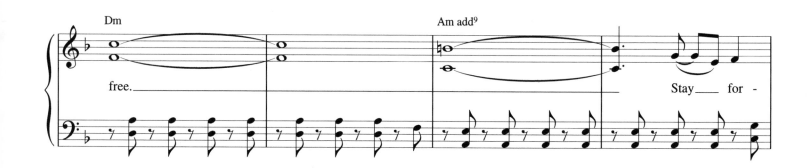

6

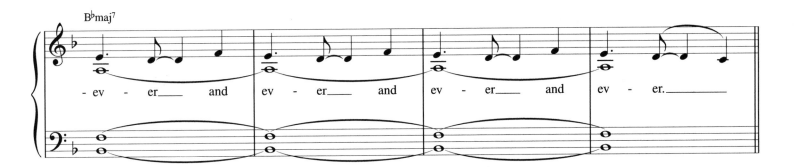

Verse 2:
There's a dark secret in me
Don't leave me locked in your heart
Set me free *etc.*

Caught In The Middle

Words & Music by Ben Adams, Paul Marazzi, Chris Porter & Rick Mitra

Moderately

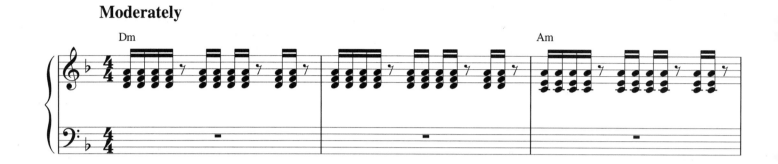

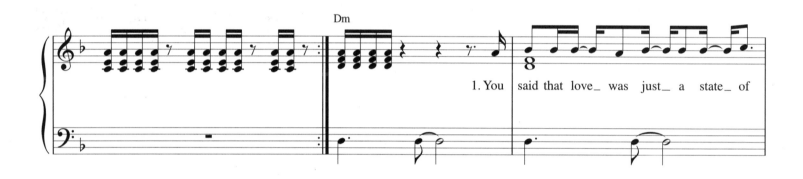

1. You said that love was just a state of

mind. A puz-zle made of piec-es you can't find. But for

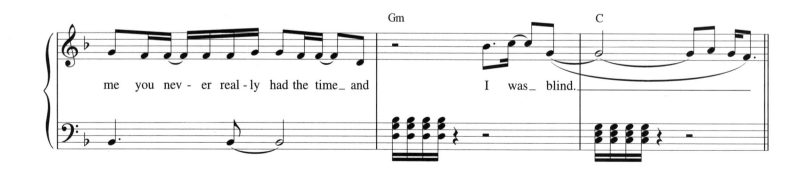

me you nev-er real-ly had the time and I was blind.

2. And ev - 'ry - thing____ that you meant to me,____
(Verse 3 see block lyric)

is writ - ten in____ the pag - es of____ my his - to - ry._____ But it's

ov - er now____ as far as I can see,

sud - den - ly_____

Things are so diff - 'rent now____ you're gone,____ I thought it'd be ea - sy, I____ was wrong.

_____ (And now____ I'm caught)____ And now I'm caught in the mid - dle.

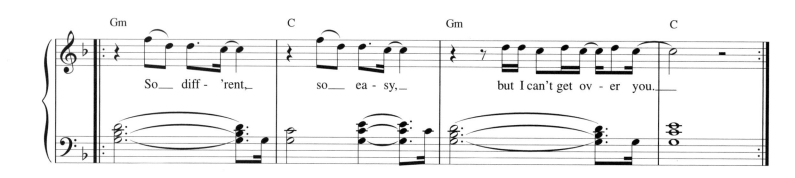

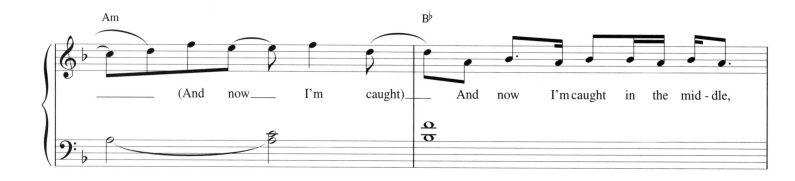

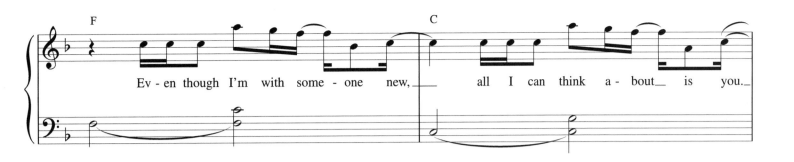

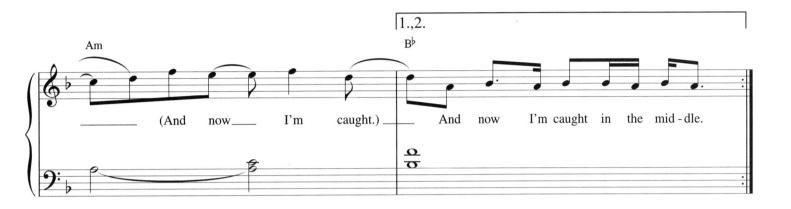

Verse 3:
Moving on, she brings me brighter days
But thoughts of you are in my mind always
Like a memory that I can't erase
It's here to stay

Things are so different *etc.*

Evergreen

Words & Music by Jörgen Elofsson, Per Magnusson & David Kreuger

Moderately

1. Eyes like a sun-rise, like a rain-fall down_ my soul. And I
(Verse 2 see block lyric)

won-der,_ I won-der why you look at me like that, what you're think-ing, what's_ be-hind._

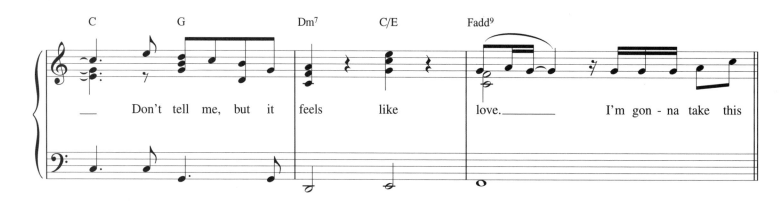

_ Don't tell me, but it feels like love._____ I'm gon-na take this

Verse 2:
Touch like an angel,
Like velvet to my skin.
And I wonder, I wonder why you wanna stay the night,
What you're dreaming, what's behind.
Don't tell me, but it feels like love.

Hero

Words & Music by Enrique Iglesias, Paul Barry & Mark Taylor

Gently

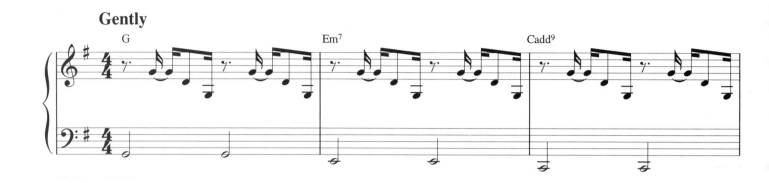

Would you dance if I asked you to dance? Would you

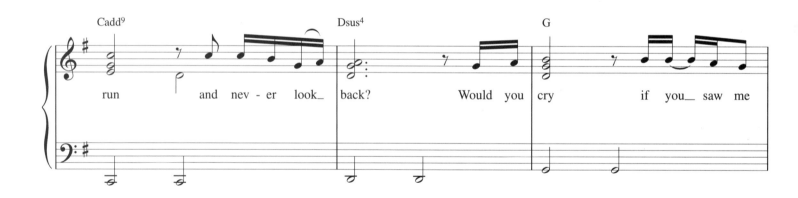

run and nev-er look_ back? Would you cry if you_ saw me

cry - ing?_ Would you save my soul to - night?_ Would you

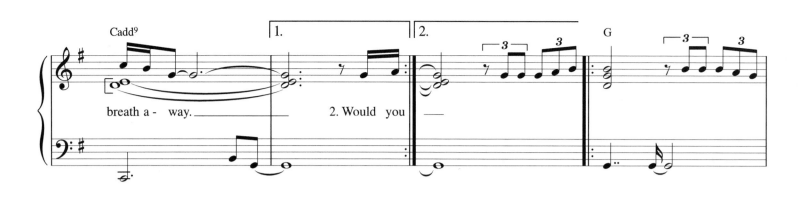

breath a - way.

2. Would you

D. $\mathsection$ al Coda

(Spoken:) Oh, I just wanna hold you,   I just wan - na hold you, oh   yeah.   My an - gel be
(Sung:)

CODA

Chorus

breath a - way.   I   can be   your he - ro ba - by.

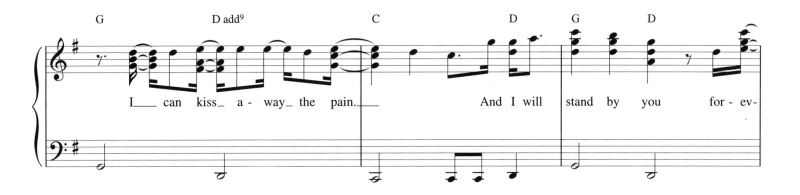

I___ can kiss___ a - way___ the pain.___ And I will stand by you for - ev-

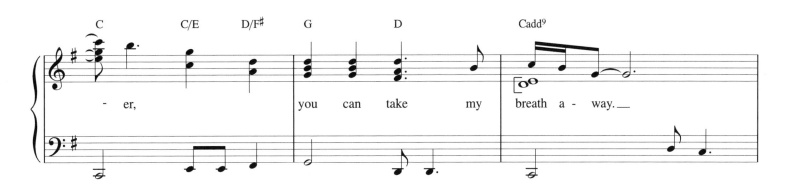

-er, you can take my breath a - way.___

rall.

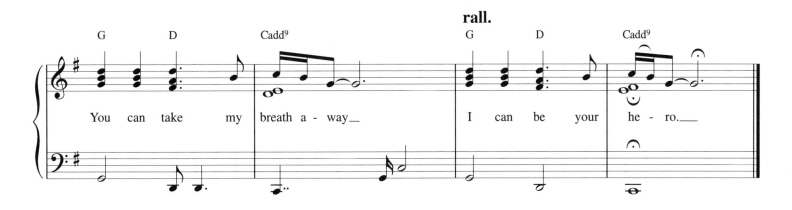

You can take my breath a - way___ I can be your he - ro.___

Verse 2:
Would you swear that you'll always be mine?
Would you lie, would you remember?
My angel be, have I lost my mind?
I don't care, you're here tonight.

Verse 3: D. 𝄉
My angel be, have I lost my mind?
Well I don't care, you're here tonight.

If You Come Back

Words & Music by Ray Ruffin, Nicole Formescu, Ian Hope & Lee Brennan

Moderate/Slow

Come on! ... Yeah! __ Can you feel me? Ba-by can you feel me?

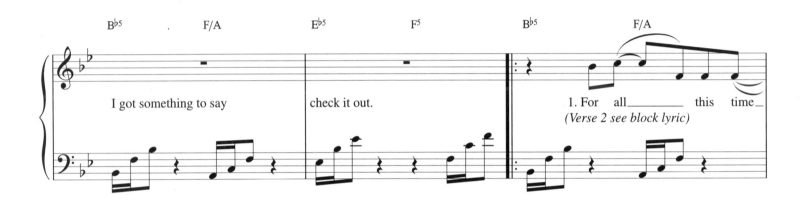

I got something to say ... check it out. ... 1. For all___ this time___
(Verse 2 see block lyric)

___ I've been lov-in' you,___ girl.___ Oh yes I have. And

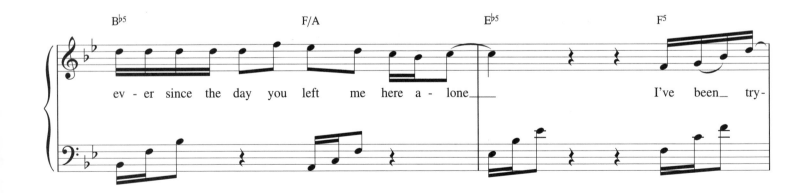

ev-er since the day you left me here a-lone___ I've been_ try-

If you come back in my life___ I'll be there till the___ end of time, oh

yeah.___ And I swear___ I'll keep you right by my side,___

Repeat to fade

___ 'cause ba - by you're the___ one I want.___ Oh yes you are,___ and I swear

Verse 2:
I watched you go
Taking my heart with you
Oh, yes you did
Every time I try to reach you on the phone
Baby, you're never there
Girl, you're never home.

So if I did something wrong *etc.*

Somethin' Stupid

Words & Music by C. Carson Parks

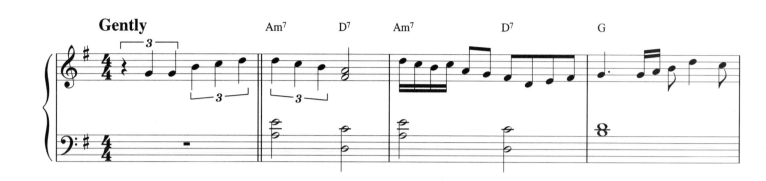

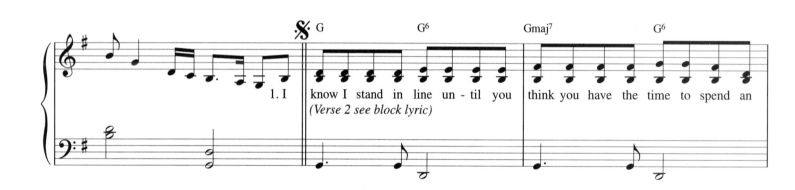

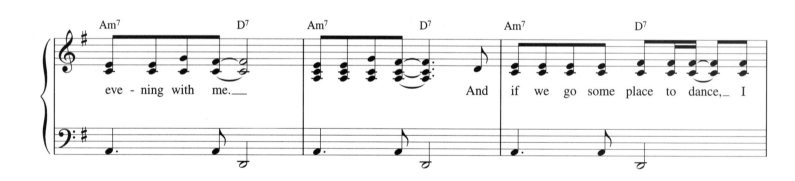

Verse 2:
I practise every day to find
Some clever lines to say
To make the meaning come true
But then I think I'll wait until
The evening gets late
And I'm alone with you
The time is right
Your perfume fills my head
The stars get red
And oh, the night's so blue
And then I go and spoil it all
By saying somethin' stupid
Like I love you.

Emotion

Words & Music by Barry Gibb & Robin Gibb

No - bo - dy left in this world to hold me tight, no - bo - dy____ to hold

me, in the world to kiss good - night, no - bo - dy_____ to kiss____

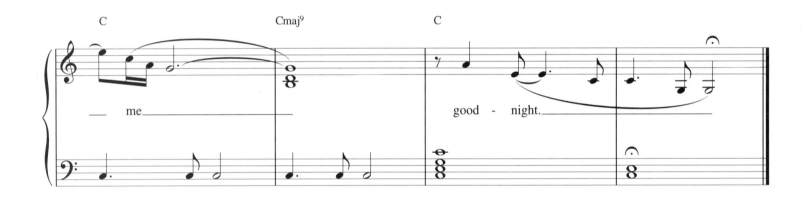

____ me____ good - night.____

Verse 2:
I'm there at your side,
I'm part of all the things you are
But you've got a part of someone else
You've got to go find your shining star.

And where are you now   *etc.*

Unchained Melody

Words by Hy Zaret
Music by Alex North

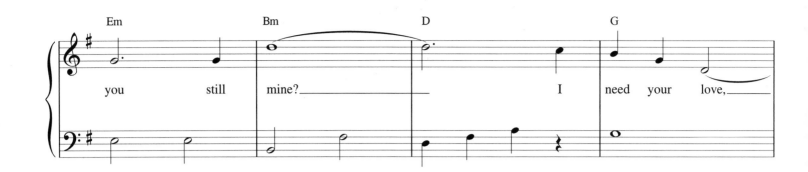

you   still   mine?_____   I   need   your love,____

To Coda ⊕

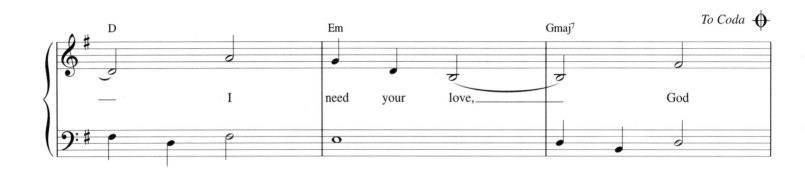

____   I   need   your love,_____   God

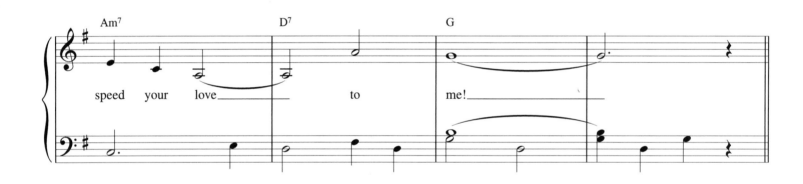

speed   your love_____   to   me!_____

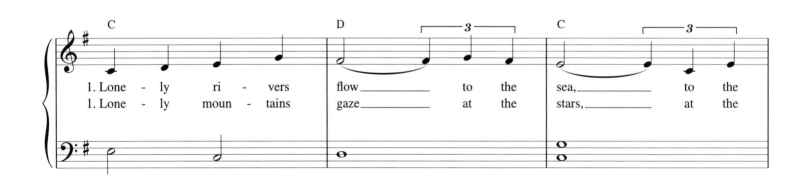

1. Lone - ly   ri - vers   flow_____ to   the   sea,_____   to   the
1. Lone - ly   moun - tains gaze_____ at   the   stars,_____ at   the

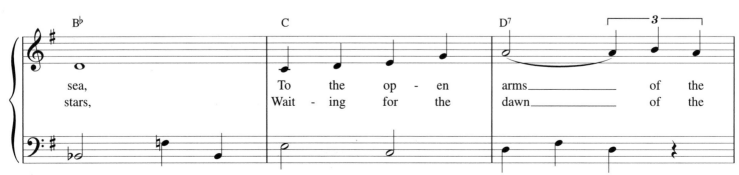

sea,   To   the   op - en   arms_____ of   the
stars,   Wait - ing for   the   dawn_____ of   the

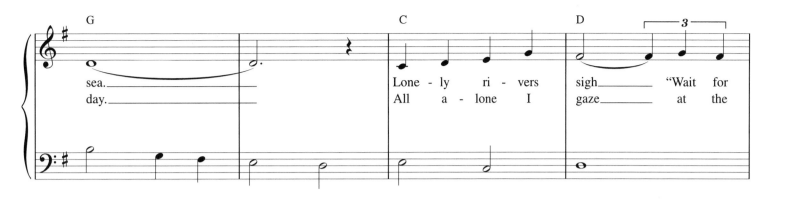

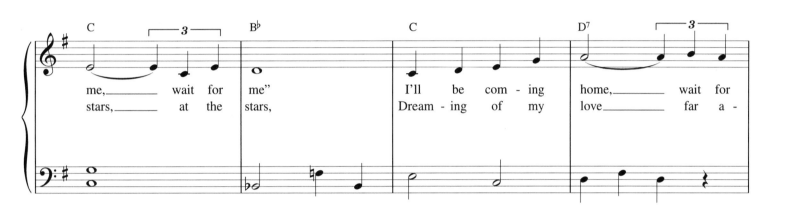

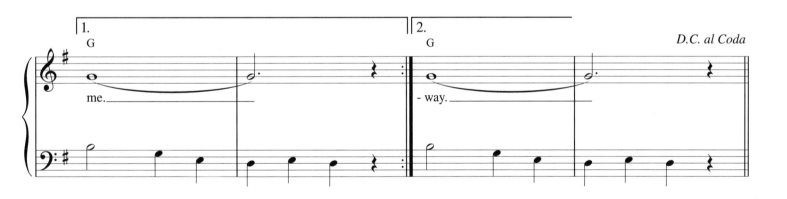

CODA

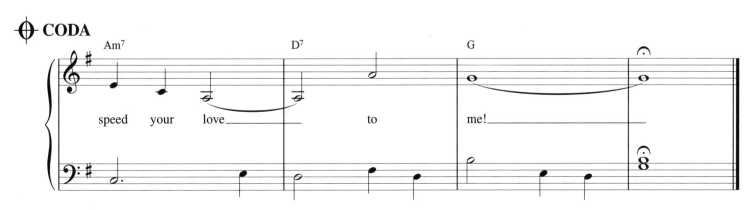

What If

Words & Music by Steve Mac & Wayne Hector

take it back,_ would you still_ be mine? 'Cause I tried but I had to draw__ the line,_

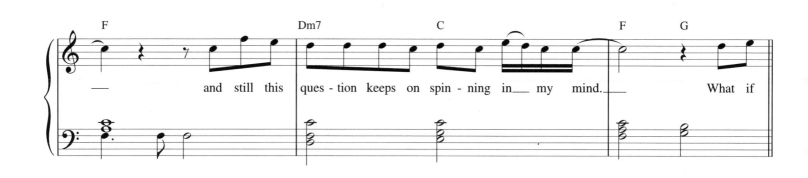

_ and still this ques - tion keeps on spin - ning in__ my mind.__ What if

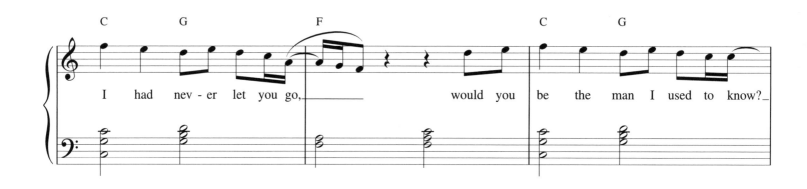

I had nev - er let you go,_____ would you be the man I used to know?

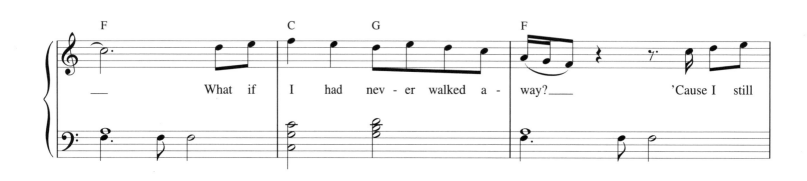

_ What if I had nev - er walked a - way?____ 'Cause I still

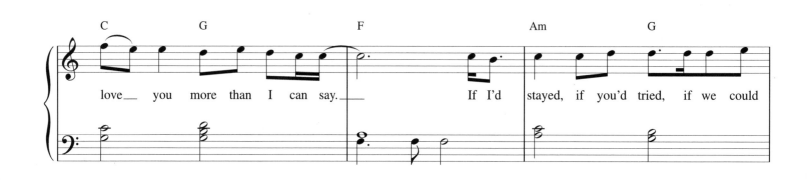

love_ you more than I can say._ If I'd stayed, if you'd tried, if we could

on - ly turn__ back time. But I guess we'll nev - er know.

We'll nev - er know.

Verse 2:
Many roads to take
Some to joy some to heartache
Anyone can lose their way
And if I said that we could turn it back
Right back to the start
Would you take the chance
And make the change?
Do you think how it would have been sometimes
Do you pray that I'd never left your side.

What if I had never let you go?   *etc.*

You

Words & Music by Eliot Kennedy, Tim Lever, Mike Percy & Tim Woodcock

You are all I need to get me through, (to get me through now ba - by.)

Like a fall - ing star I fell for you (I fell for you.)

1. Sweet an - ti - ci - pa - tion is giv - ing me the but - ter - flies
(Verses 2 & 3 see block lyric)

And my heart-beat's pac - ing 'cause lov - ing you is beau - ti - ful, when

an - gel sent__ from high__ a - bove,__ and now I know__ that all__ I need__ is

Verse 2:
I thought I new what love was
It always ended up in tears
It's just the way my world was
Until you walked into my life
It's something that I just can't hide.

Bridge 2:
Real love has come my way
And I know it's here to stay
And it feels like never before
'Cause loving you's so beautiful baby.

Verse 3:
You're my inspiration,
My world just seems a brighter place.
I just wanna tell you
I've never felt this way,
I never thought I'd see the day.

Bridge 3:
Real love has come my way
And I know it's here to stay
And it feels like never before
'Cause loving you's so beautiful baby.

World Of Our Own

Words & Music by Steve Mac & Wayne Hector

Moderate/Slow

1. You make me feel fun - ny,
(Verse 2 see block lyric)
when

you come a - round,__ yeah, that's what I found__ out, hon - ey.
What am I

do - ing with - out__ you? You make me feel hap - py, when I

All of the things I've been__ look - ing for, have al - ways been here out- side__ of my door, and

all of the time I'm look - ing for some - thing new. What am I do - ing with - out__ you?

1.

What am I do - ing with - out__ you?__

2.

2. Well I guess I'm Well, it's feel - ing right__ now, so let's do it right__ now.

Pray - ing that some - how you will__ un - der - stand the

46

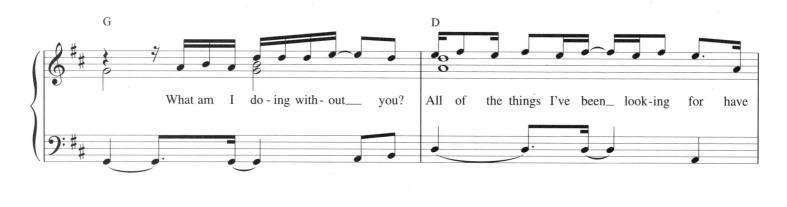

What am I do-ing with-out___ you? All of the things I've been___ look-ing for have

al - ways been here out - side___ of my door, and all of the time I'm look - ing for some - thing

new. (World of___ our own.)___ new, what am I do - ing with - out___ you?___

Verse 2:
Well I guess I'm ready
For settling down
And fooling around is over
And I swear that it's true
No buts or maybe's
When I'm falling down
There's always someone saves me
And girl it's you
Funny how life can
Be so surprising
I'm just realising what you do.

We got a little world of our own   *etc.*